DISCARD

# "ANIMALS
## OF IRELAND"
### IN MYTH & LEGEND

Dáithí Ó hÓgáin

# INTRODUCTION

The other creatures with whom we share the world have always been a source of interest and of fantasy for the human race. People have been close observers of animals and their traits, have imagined that they possess a kind of intelligence which parallels human intelligence, inclinations which parallel human ones. These are the reasons why so many entertaining stories and fables have been invented about animals, and in this Ireland has an especially rich harvest. The capacity of our fourfooted friends and foes to inspire scholars and storytellers has indeed been obvious at all stages of Irish tradition. The narratives in this little book are selected from the ancient epical lore, and they are retold with an eye to their central motifs and their dramatic content.

Dáithí Ó hÓgáin

Is gaoth ar muir mé, is tonn treathan ar tír,
is fuaim mhara, is damh seacht ndíreann,
is seabhac in aill, is deor gréine, is caoin,
is torc ar ghail mé, is eo i linn...

-words attributed to the ancient seer Amhairghin

I am wind on the sea, a strong wave on the land,
the noise of the wave, and a stag with seven antler-tips,
I am a hawk on a cliff, a drop of sundew, beautiful,
I am a wild boar in courage, a salmon in a pool...

# GUIDE TO PRONUNCIATION

The nearest equivalent in English spelling is indicated in each case. The sound intended by ' kh ' is a fricative ' k ', like the final sound in Scottish ' loch ' or the ' ch ' in German. The stress is normally put on the first syllable of a word :-

| | |
|---|---|
| BLÁTH DEARG | " blaw darrog " |
| BRAN | " bron " |
| CAOILTE | " kweelta " |
| CIARÁN | " keearawn " |
| CORMAC MAC AIRT | " kurmock mock art " |
| CU CHULAINN | " koo khullen " |
| DÁIRE | " daw-erra " |
| DIARMAID | " deearmid " |
| DONN | " dun ", also " down " |
| FIONN MAC CUMHAILL | " f-yun mock kool ", also " finn " and " f-yoon " |
| GLAS | " gloss " |
| GOIBHNIU | " gwiv-new " |
| GUAIRE | " goo-erra " |
| IORUSÁN | " irrusawn " |
| MACHA | " mokha " |
| MEADHBH | " mayv " |
| OISÍN | " usheen ", also " esh-een " |
| SEANCHÁN | " shanakhawn " |
| SAINGLIU | " sanglew " |

ULSTER

Lough Derg

Navan Fort ●

● Fews

Cooley

CONNACHT

Rathcroghan ●

LEINSTER

● Knowth

● Tara

▲ Slieve Callan

MUNSTER

Beare

Crow Island

# COW

There was a famous smith in Ireland long ago and his name was Goibhniu. He had forges in many parts of the country and, since he was a magically swift traveller, he had little difficulty in giving his services to the people of each area. His best-known smithy was on the Beare peninsula in the south-west of the country, and it is said that he resided on the tiny Crow Island there.

He had a cow called the Glas, which means 'light-grey'. This cow was a great milker, and was also a very agile animal. When she desired to taste the green grass of the mainland she jumped over the chasm from Crow Island to the Reen promontory - a distance of twenty yards. The fame of the cow as a milker reached to all parts of Ireland, and a certain jealous woman boasted that she had a vessel which the Glas could not fill. The vessel was a sieve. The Glas yielded a vast quantity of milk, enough to fill a lake, but still it ran through the sieve. Eventually, the great cow began to weaken, and she died from her efforts to fill the impossible vessel.

# BULL

**D**onn was the name of the great brown bull which grazed in the Cooley Mountains. It was fierce and strong, and so huge that thirty boys could ride on its back. Not only the human people of this world were in awe of this mighty animal, but otherworld powers also, and no evil spirits would come into the district where it was. The Donn was owned by a farmer called Dáire, and it was the great mainstay of his herd, for it could bull fifty heifers in a single day.

The ambitious queen Meadhbh of Connacht assembled a vast army to invade Ulster and take Donn, for her husband had a massive white bull which she could not match from her herds. As that army approached, the war-goddess came in the form of a bird and alighted on the post near where the Donn was grazing. The bird spoke to the bull and warned it to go with its heifers to a safe place. Notwithstanding this, Meadhbh's army managed to capture the brown bull of Cooley, and they drove it west across the river Shannon into Connacht.

When they reached Meadhbh's court at Rathcroghan, the brown bull of Cooley rejoiced at the fine pasture there and bellowed three times. The white bull heard this, and realising that a rival was at hand, rushed furiously to the encounter. The assembled crowd watched with bated breath as the two mighty animals clashed. The brown bull placed its hoof on the horn of the other and held it there for a long time. Eventually this lock was broken, and the goring began. All day long the ferocious contest went on, and it continued after darkness fell. Trampling plains and forests, the bulls travelled all over Ireland, rending and tearing each other, as the people huddled in their cabins listening to the snorting and crashing outside.

When morning came, the brown bull was seen passing by Rathcroghan, with the carcase of the white held high on its horns. Itself mortally wounded, the Donn then headed back home to Cooley. Seeing the fields and mountains there, and its favourite cow waiting, the great bull was overcome with emotion. It leaned against a mound, its heart came through its mouth in a black clot of blood, and it died.

# HORSE

The grey of Macha was the magnificent chariot-horse of the hero Cú Chulainn. It was said that the hero had been passing one day by the lake in the Fews mountains when he first saw the steed. It was coming towards him from the water, and Cú Chulainn wasted no time in putting his two arms around its neck and leaping onto its back. The horse started wildly, but Cú Chulainn remained astride it and an epical battle of wills began between man and beast. The grey coursed around all Ireland until in the evening Cú Chulainn brought it back tamed to the royal capital of Ulster, Navan Fort.

Soon after, Cú Chulainn acquired another great steed, called the Black of Saingliu. In all his great battles, the Grey and the Black drew his chariot fiercely through the enemy armies, racing furiously and kicking and biting the foe.

The Grey was very intelligent and always obedient to its master. When Cú Chulainn was tricked to go into an ambush by his enemies, however, the horse sensed that misfortune lay ahead, and refused to be caught and tackled. When Cú Chulainn approached it bolted away, and great tears of blood came from its eyes and fell onto its forefeet. Then the charioteer of Cú Chulainn came and spoke softly to it, saying that it must be with its master on this day above all others. Only then did the Grey consent to be put under the chariot along with the Black .

Three magical spears had been prepared by his foes to slay Cú Chulainn. The first of these struck his charioteer, and the Grey was transfixed by the second. Cú Chulainn wrenched the spear from the horse's body but was himself struck a mortal blow by the third spear. The faithful steed came and lay its head in the breast of the dead hero, and then raced away from the battlefield and did not stop until it reached the waters of the lake from which it had come.

# CAT

The poet Seanchán was a very peevish and a very demanding man. When he was being entertained in the palace of the Connacht king Guaire, he refused to eat the food, claiming that the mice had left the imprint of their teeth on it. He then began to satirise the mice, and so powerful was his poetry that ten of the little creatures dropped dead in his presence. The poet next decided to satirise the cats for not controlling the mice. He singled out the king of the cats, Iorusán, calling him the fellow with the monstrous claws and ugly jagged ears who could not catch a mouse.

Iorusán heard of this in his cave at Knowth. He was a huge beast, with a mighty chest, thick snout, razor-like claws and teeth, and was panting with anger at the news. He went to where Seanchán was, seized the poet, flung him over his shoulder, and set out for home with the terrified captive. St Ciarán was working in his forge as they passed by, and he threw a red-hot piece of iron at the cat, which was thus forced to release the troublesome poet.

# DEER

The hero Fionn Mac Cumhaill married a beautiful girl called Bláth Dearg. Time passed, and she was expecting a baby when Fionn was called away to battle. When he returned to his fortress, great was his grief to find that his young wife had been stolen away by a cunning magician. Fionn immediately set out in search of her, and continued to search for seven whole years, but all his efforts to locate her were in vain.

Then it happened that he went hunting early with his hounds and, through the mist of the morning, they saw a white doe. The hounds immediately took up the chase, through thickets and through brambles, until they and their quarry disappeared from sight. Fionn ran on after them as fast as he could, and he soon heard great howling in the distance. In a forest-clearing, he found the hounds gathered in a circle, snarling and with the hair standing straight on their necks. In the centre of the circle was a handsome young boy, with long hair growing to his shoulders and no fear in his face.

Hushing his hounds aside, Fionn took the strange boy by the hand and asked him who he was and what had brought him there. The boy told him that, just before his birth, his mother had been stolen away by a cruel magician, who had turned her into a deer. Fionn knew then that this was his son, and he named him Oisín, which means 'little fawn'.

Oisín further told his father that, when he was born in the mountains, the doe began to lick him. She gave one sweep of her tongue over his temple, and a tuft of deer's hair grew there at once. Seeing this, however, she had enough of the woman's nature left in her that she wished her son to be a man. So she stopped licking him, and he grew up as a human being like his father.

Fionn brought Oisín home with him, and the boy grew up to be a great and wise man, but the timid white doe was never seen again.

# HOUND

**B**ran was the favourite hound of Fionn. Not only was it a great hunter, but it was also a great personal friend, and always sat behind Fionn at feasts. When the hero talked and sang on such occasions, Bran would bark and whine in unison.

It was a huge and beautiful hound. The tallest of the other dogs would pass under its groin without stooping, and its head was as high as Fionn's shoulder. It had two white sides, purple haunches, four blue feet, green paws with red nails, and a proud eye in its fine head. It was the fleetest of hounds, being able to catch up with four hares running in different directions, and Fionn used to boast that 'no deer or boar ever raced upon a plain' but Bran could bring them down. It was also very faithful, and often, when Fionn and his men had failed in the hunt and were weary and hungry after their exertions, Bran would slip away from them to the forest and return with their meal.

Bran fought fiercely for its master whenever that was necessary. Fionn was once engaged in a battle to the death with a great water-monster at Lough Derg, and the monster was beginning to gain the advantage when Bran leapt into its open maw and began to bite at its insides, thus allowing Fionn the opportunity to slay it.

On another occasion, a strange warrior leading a huge black hound arrived and mockingly challenged Fionn's company to a fight. The black hound was a ferocious creature, breathing fire through its mouth, but Bran immdiately began to yelp to show that it was willing to defend the honour of Fionn. The fight between the two animals was terrible, with Bran being badly bitten and mauled. It could not properly defend itself, because one of its paws was covered with a silver shoe. Eventually Fionn's friend Diarmaid pulled the hounds apart, so that the shoe could be removed, and then Bran slew its opponent.

Fionn rose one morning and went to hunt on Slieve Callan, a place which had a great number of deer. He did not wish to alarm the quarry too soon, and thus had Bran held in a tight leash and warned the hound to be quiet. Seeing some wonderful red deer, however, Bran could no longer restrain itself but began to bay.

Seized by a sudden bout of anger at this, Fionn lashed out at the hound and so severe was the blow that the leash became embedded in its head. Bran gave a surprised look at its master, and for long remained so until great tears began to roll from its eyes. Then it suddenly jerked the leash, breaking the silver collar, and fled quickly away. It raced along the mountainside until, reaching a lake, it made a great leap into the water and was drowned.

Ever after, when Fionn heard the barking of any dog, his heart was filled with sorrow.

# FOX

It happened once that Fionn quarrelled with the high-king of Ireland, Cormac Mac Airt, and as a result Cormac had him imprisoned. One of Fionn's best friends was Caoilte, who was a marvellous runner and who was determined to secure the hero's release. He therefore began to disrupt the affairs of the kingdom in every possible way, by letting calves go to the cows, by setting the horses loose, by burning mills and kilns, and by tying up the king's officials as they went about their business.

Cormac did not relent, and then Caoilte went disguised into the royal fortress of Tara, seized the king, and demanded to know what ransom would free Fionn. Cormac stated his terms - a male and female of every type of animal to be brought to him on the lawn of Tara. Caoilte set out to herd all the animals as required, and by his fleetness of foot succeeded in bringing them in one great straggling drove to Tara. The astounded Cormac had to release Fionn, and then he enquired of Caoilte which animal gave him the most trouble. ' Well,' said Caoilte, ' I had particular difficulty with the fox!'

# MYTHS & LEGENDS OF IRELAND SERIES

## KINGS OF IRELAND

## QUEENS OF IRELAND

## ANIMALS OF IRELAND

## HEROES OF IRELAND

REAL IRELAND

© REAL IRELAND DESIGN LIMITED
Front Cover Design: Joe Reynolds
Text: Dáithí Ó hÓgáin MA PhD
Layout: Target Marketing Ltd.

ANIMALS OF IRELAND
IN MYTH AND LEGEND
ISBN 0 946887 01 2